True Love

Posy Simmonds

Fontana/Collins

First published in Great Britain
by Jonathan Cape Ltd 1981
First issued in Fontana Paperbacks 1983

Copyright © Posy Simmonds 1981

Made and printed in Great Britain
by William Collins Sons & Co. Ltd,
Glasgow

LOVE

It is a few days before Christmas. In the deserted office sits Janice Brady clasping a jar of stilton to her breast. She has been in love for the last five minutes.

She is in love with the Creative Director of Beazeley & Buffin Advertising....

Oh Stanhope!

Was it only this afternoon that their eyes had held each other....in the Conference Room, where all the staff had assembled to sing carols to Mr Beazeley?

♪ Frosty wind made moan....♫

She'd been standing at the front, feeling a bit of a lemon.....

♪ Brr-ring me flesh & br-ring me wine!

...and Mr Wright...Stanhope had WINKED at her!

And afterwards, he'd handed her a mulled wine & said in his lovely, educated voice:

Here, this should fill both **bilges**, Janice!

Thank God, that's over

And much later, when she'd gone back upstairs to fetch her coat....

Oh God! Someone's coming!

Ssh! GIGGLE

...Mr Wright was sitting there alone in the dark!

Oh, hallo...er..Janice...just..er **checking SECURITY**...can't be too sure who's in the building during a **party**, can we?

There's a lot of quite valuable stuff up here...well, all the..er Christmas presents from my clients...**BOTTLES** and so on..

Here, have a **stilton** & a Happy Christmas!

Then he was gone.

Greetings

Bliss Associates

STILTON

He was waiting for **ME**..... ...to give me this............... ...**He fancies me!** WOW!

True Love

Janice Brady dreams of Mr Wright.

She dreams of their next meeting, when all will be different: she will be wearing her new *disco pants* & shiny *V-neck*.

She will be wearing that frilly top and the *stilettos*......

....and lots & lots of *Ivoire Beige Cover-up Foundation*.

JANICE DREAMS SHE'S COLLECTING MR WRIGHT'S EMPTY TEA CUP. IT IS WELL AFTER SIX ON AN EVENING LIT WITH STARS.

COME.

STANHOPE DRAINED HIS TEA......

YOU'RE WORKING LATE, JANICE...ISN'T IT KNOCKING-OFF TIME?

BUT TODAY THERE WAS A FLASH OF CONCERN IN HIS SAILOR-BLUE EYES.

SHE WAS TREMBLING...BUT NOT FROM COLD.

YOU OK, JANICE? YOU LOOK AS GLUM AS A MUSTARD POT...

HER HEART BEAT LIKE AN IMPRISONED BIRD....

WHAT IS IT? TELL ME...

...I'VE OFTEN WONDERED HOW YOU FELT, JANICE...

JUST ONE BREATHLESS, ASKING LOOK...AND THEN ALL AT ONCE HIS ARMS WERE AROUND HER....

A TONGUE OF LAMBENT FLAME SCORCHED THROUGH HER....

HER LASHES BEAT LIKE IMPRISONED MOTHS.

HIS VOICE WAS HARSH.

HE PALED BENEATH HIS TAN...HIS VOICE WAS NOT QUITE STEADY.

SHE SWAYED....FAINT WITH GRATITUDE: HE UNDERSTOOD!

...AND NOW HE WAS PROMISING HER THE LOVE SHE HAD ALWAYS DREAMED OF....

..A PURE FLAME OF CONCUPISCENCE BURNING FOREVER IN THE CATHEDRAL OF HIS HEART!

Romance

It is lunch time. In the saloon of **The Brass Monk**, Stanhope Wright chats up one of his Creative Dept.

...but you **KNOW** that, Vicky, don't you? Don't pretend you don't....

What?

YOU KNOW that I really *fancy* you, don't you?

Look, I *must* get back.... It's nearly 2·30...

...but you *will* have dinner with me..?

I might.

I'll send you a memo...

Stanhope is filled with a suave excitement. He anticipates another *successful* *Chasse au Coeur*....

Madame...I sound my horn...You have five minutes' start!

Ooh·la·la!

Tiens! Chanel No.5!

THE MEET

PICKING UP THE SCENT

Jealousy

In the early evening of a certain day, Janice Brady lies in wait for Mr Wright....

She has been in love now for *several* weeks.

In a moment, she reasons, HE will emerge from his office & *chance* upon her.

But Mr Wright is *not* alone. He has been *in conference* with Victoria Medlicott , discussing the impending *production* of a *canned soup* commercial....

Mmm...*basically*, Vicky, I'm happy with the script... *Cabot Findlater* have done a *GREAT* job...but there're just *one or two* little...

Well, it's not engraved in granite, yet...

Well, doesn't she.. kind of... **MIND?** You know, because I'm really **not** into that whole sort of bit... you know, ...lies... **HOSTILITY**....

Listen...I never have to lie to my wife!

I don't believe in it...

It's not worth it....

...I mean, I **ADORE** my wife...we have a very civilised relationship & we both lead our own lives...

She wouldn't **DREAM** of **wondering** where I was!

Now...can I **drop** you somewhere?

Yeah... all right... ......

Swing doors usher the couple out. Crushed & desolated, Janice is obliged to take a chocolate biscuit.

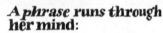

A phrase runs through her mind:

"I think we should do it at my place in the country..."

Hitherto, Janice has disbelieved *office gossip* concerning the *rakish* aspects of Mr Wright's character. Now she realises it is probably true.

Pig!

The purpose of the *sheep* eludes her. But it does not sound nice.

Poor little things!

And his POOR WIFE!!

She remembers the photos on Mr Wright's desk... ...his second wife, Trish, their baby son, Willy and Jocasta, the daughter of his first marriage....

Janice puts on her fun fur and goes home.

But **why** the **SHEEP?**

Rêves d'amour

After supper with her parents, Janice retires to her room.

Fossicking in her vast handbag for some chocolate, she touches the jar of Stilton...

Janice imagines...a glittering social event, when she will cut Stanhope *stone dead*.....

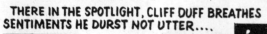

> SIGH

> SNIFF

Oh stanhope! *Ah Vicky!*

> ?

Although Revenge is sweet, unrequited Love needs a nobler finale.....

JANICE IMAGINES THAT **STANHOPE & VICKY** ARE IN *DEADLY PERIL*.... (THEY HAVE JUST GONE ABOUT THEIR MYSTERIOUS BUSINESS WITH THOSE *SHEEP*.....)

> HELP!
> BAAA BAAA!
> BAA!

WORRIED SICK, THE SHEEP HAVE BEGUN TO CUT UP ROUGH.....

> BAA!
> MAAA!
> BAA!
> Bah!

A Climate of Implicit Trust

It is late one Friday night. Stanhope returns home....

...to discover his wife in bed with an art catalogue..................

(*She is translating it from the German.*) She hums to herself.

What I mean is...in a moment of....weakness... I asked *Vicky Medlicott* out to dinner...I'm sorry... I do...er...I *did* find her very...attractive...and afterwards, I'm afraid..er...things got a bit out of hand....um...at her flat...

...but she's very sensible ...& we talked it out...& agreed to call a halt......

And that's as far as it's gone... I promise...That's it...*FINITO.*

Dear Stanhope!

mm...I knew you'd understand, Trish...you're so *wonderful.*

mm

Aren't you going to tell me about *sheep?*

?

SHEEP? What sheep?

I don't know, Stanhope.... one of your secretaries rang... *Janice*, that's right...wanted to have a word with you...

Janice?

...seemed very worried about what you and *Vicky Medlicott* were planning to do to *sheep...*

Weather Forecast

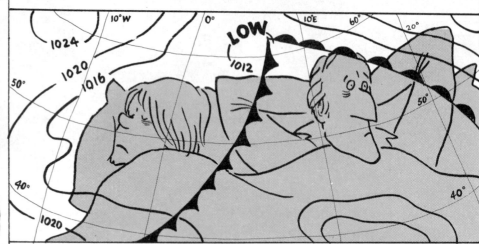

During the evening a warm front has passed over Central and Northern Stanhope, but this is followed by a deep depression moving in from the West. The chart shows a potentially thundery situation developing, probably reaching the Continental Quilt by morning, when one can expect some violent convective activity.

Outlook: Turning colder with frost in sheltered places

Lighting-up Time: 6·07am

Lovers' Tryst

Spring arrives.

Stanhope cannot ignore the pulsing of sap...

After deciding not to remove the child seat from the back of his car

...Stanhope drives out of town.....

....to where the grass is lush....

Cautionary Tales

One evening, in the street....

Look, Vicky, you **know** how difficult weekends are for me...I **CAN'T** see you then...

I have to look after my **son**...anyway, my wife would smell a rat...

Tsk!

Look, **far** be it for **ME** to **foul up** things between you and your wife!

WHO was it who gave me this **big spiel** about his wonderful **Open Marriage**? Eh?

It's become a real **DRAG** hanging around for you, Stanhope....

Oh **Vicky!**

I'll make it up to you..promise!

Good Lord!

Stanhope!

!

Oh, hi **George**...Wendy... How're you?

we've just been to see the new **Brummer** movie, "Liszt, Comme Liste Electorale"...

Listen, d'you want to join us for a quick one at the **Diver**?

Er.. I'd **love** to another day... um.. I'm afraid I've got to go & talk **SHOP** with my **colleague**, here......

Stanhope & Vicky vanish into the night.....

Shop! My **foot**!

Old devil!

Isn't **she** the one Trish told us about?

Yes!

Looks as though she's giving him a hard time

They're always so much younger than him, aren't they?

They **are**... I wouldn't fancy someone **much younger**... would **YOU**, Nick?

No... not much...

I remember I felt **SO** proud of myself...

...especially after last time....

...Here am I... a married man... **fit & 45**... in a borrowed flat... preparing to embrace a beautiful girl, 25 years my junior...

Here am I, emerged **TRIUMPHANT**...

...From **MID-LIFE CRISIS**... looking **GOOD**, feeling **GREAT**!

Here I am, an erstwhile victim of **FLAB** and middle-aged **TORPOR**... having pulled my **SOCKS** up

...Having given up starch, sugar, ciggies & Scotch.. having just lost **2** stone & found a waist... having lowered my cholesterol count & improved my muscle tone...

...having discovered that one's stomach is only so big... like a little **BOWL**

...having begun the day with a glass of hot water & 30 press ups... having lunched on **2** spoonfuls of **BRAN** & a green salad... having dined on spinach & Malvern water...

GURGLE LURGLE GLOOGLE LOOOGLE LURGLE GURGLE GURGLE

Hmm

Hmm..yes...think they're all rather a *liability*...

What are?

We-ll, *young people*... one's relationship with them........ there's this business at the *Poly*... very *disturbing*....

..This *student*... *Gabby*... got hauled up before the *Appeals Board*....

FAST

ALL BEEF HAMBU

We-ll, she'd been in trouble all her **2nd year**...didn't do the compulsory essays...*failed* to keep contact with her *tutor*...

Anyway, I met Gabby just before she went in to see the *Board*...

The *Appeals Board*'ll **SLING** me out, George, won't they? *Oh God*... *I hate* myself!

Well, that's only a speculative notion, Gabby...*Selbsthass* won't help you...

☆彡!☆!

But Gabby...you see, you **HAVEN'T** pro- duced the *work*..

They had to turn down your *Robbe-Grillet FILMOGRAPHY* ...it's not consecutive prose.

I supported the argument of *BUTOR*ian precedent..

Not to mention *RABELAIS*!

And I pointed out that your *"Faux Bons of the Faubourgs"* had..... some surprising aperçus

P. Simmonds 1979 After W.F.Yeames, with apologies

Married Love

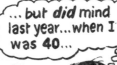

*40...
Oh God...*

*'Don't suppose I'll ever do **THAT** again in a **cinema**...*

Never again go to a film & **miss** most of it... *SIGH*....

I love you

...& no one'll look at me like that ever again..

...thank God!...Had my lot...no more spotty youths breathing tobacco...no more suffocating clinches... just a middle-aged **MUM** now... **mature student**... mother of **Six**...... *SIGH*....

*... count my **blessings**.... ...dear **George**...*

SNIFF

Never again have someone **smell** of **TOOTHPASTE** especially for **ME**.... ...*SNIFF...SNIFF*....

SNIFF

What is it?

TUNNEL OF LOVE

Janice is on her way to work.

In the crowded carriage, she finds herself next to Dave, from the office. They have never really spoken before....

A little light reading matter helps to pass the time....

Caveat Emptor

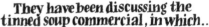

At Beazeley & Buffin Advertising, a meeting draws to a close....

Make some coffee, Janice, there's a good girl.

They have been discussing the tinned soup commercial, in which....

...Originally.....

...a man & his young son would be seen enjoying a walk in the un-changing countryside....

...They climb a hill, pretending it's Mount Everest. At the summit, they broach the <u>Chunky Pottage</u>.

A sound makes them start.
Is it a YETI?

No, it's an old shepherd, eating <u>his</u> <u>Chunky Pottage</u>...

....because: "Tis just like a soup arter taste!"

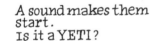

"**Mr Daly said:** <u>I SEE IT ALL!</u> We open on the <u>DAD & LAD</u> striding off...<u>CUT BACK</u> to farmhouse kitchen, warm & cosy...we'll have red gel on the brutes ...<u>MUM</u> smiles as she heats soup on the AGA...there's a little girl...make it a <u>REAL</u> family...she helps MUM...maybe she holds the can. CUT to the guys climbing the hill...CUT BACK to MUM filling the thermos with soup...little girl looks on. We get a lot of <u>LOVE</u> in this shot. CUT to the guys opening the thermos at the top of the hill...<u>lotta smiles!</u> Then we go into product sequence...voice over.. something like: CHUNKY POTTAGE...MUM <u>KNOWS</u> it's good...it's made from big, hearty, meaty chunx, in a rich gravy environment...gives them energy to go all day!"

" And we see the guys coming home in the evening light. MUM & the little girl welcome them at the door. CUT to beauty shot of product...MUM's hand pats it appreciatively. **Mr Katz, Mr Morton-Berry, Mr Baker & Mr Wright** all said they went a bundle on this idea. **Vicky Medlicott said:** Oh God, does it <u>have</u> to be the <u>mother</u> making the soup? **Mr Conway said:** Couldn't the <u>DAD</u> make the soup while the <u>MUM</u> read the paper?

"**Mr Katz said:** Does that happen in your home, Harry? Does your wife sit around while you make soup? **Mr Conway said:** Haa! No way! **Mr Daly said:** Anyway, I hate using men in kitchens...all those problems trying to make them not look GAY. **Mr McShane said:** Yeah! **Mr Morton-Berry said:** And at the end of the day, when all's said and done, a kitchen looks an unnatural sort of place without a MOTHER in it, I think we'd all agree. **Mr Daly said.....**"

L'après-midi d'un Fawn Raincoat

One perfect day, after an early start & bacon sandwiches, Cabot Findlater begin shooting the commercial at Stanhope's gem of a XVI th century cottage.

Several people from Beazeley & Buffin are present...

...including Janice, who has come to watch. (*Mr Beazeley likes his staff to have a complete understanding of the business.*)

OK..that was perfect! We'll print that take...now, let's do it one more time for *luck*..

The day wears on. Janice begins to think about lunch.

Oh *hell*, this is bloody *hopeless*!

Anyone seen Stanhope Wright?

He's gone to have a picnic lunch in the wood... I saw him go.....

OK, listen, whats your name... *Janice*.. be an angel & find him... Ask him if it's OK to *LOSE* this *WINDOW*.

Lose that old window?

Yeah, I mean we want to take it right *OUT*.... tell him I need to get a longer-angled *SHOT*..... OK?

OK

Janice hurries off towards the wood, where she has seen Stanhope disappear with a hamper.

.. lose the window 'cos of the longer-angled shot... lose the window 'cos of the...

At the murmur of voices, Janice pauses.....

A little way off, Stanhope has spread his Burberry...

!

It is a scene of *intense* poetry...

Janice is transfixed. She cannot *quite* make out what is being said.

Well, *that's* NICE...so it's GOODBYE is it?

Yes

And I thought we were having fun...

Oh yeah, *GREAT FUN!* When-ever I was *squeezed* into your *tight schedules*..!

OK..well if that's the way you want it...

We might as well finish the picnic, then. What about some *strawberries*?

Try some *Beaumes-de-Venise* with them... "absolute *NECTAR*"!

Or what about some *pepper brie*?

Oh God! It's not my day! ...forgotten the *bloody cheese!*

Janice starts.....

How opportune of Stanhope to forget the cheese! An idea occurs to her which would both announce her presence *and* enhance the idyllic scenario.

Of course! The cheese!

Sorry about that, Vicky

Delving in her handbag she finds the jar of stilton....

STILTON

A tiny push should *send* it rolling gently down the grassy slope to arrive, as if by magic, between the two *amoureux*...

DONK!

THUNK!

Stanhope falls back senseless onto his raincoat.

Vicky is busy loosening his tie...

Oh *Christmas!*

Is he dead?

He's stunned.... What you do that for?!

Poor Stanhope!

I was just about to tell him what a swine he is...

...and now he'll never know...

Soon Stanhope opens his eyes...& is greeted by a double vision...

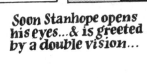

Ah! He's OK!

Thank God for that!

Home Truths

It is the evening. Stanhope reclines on his sofa feeling wretched..... partly from the bump on his head, which received hospital treatment that afternoon....

..... partly, from explaining to his colleagues how the accident had come about....

(...some of the camera crew had sniggered.)

...partly, from breaking-up with Vicky... (but then she'd become very *tedious* lately, always bringing *her* scruples & *his* wife into *everything.*)......

But most of all, Stanhope feels wretched for having just misled Trish...

God! What've you done to your head?

Oh it's nothing....piece of filming equipment fell on it.....

How kind she's been... ...how concerned....

Ye..es...

Trish...

Look, Trish...I...er.. think I want you to know...er...

Oh not again Stanhope...

I don't want to know...I'm *NOT* your *Mother Confessor*...

But I must tell you, Trish! It's important...

Just now I told you a *lie*.. ...about my *HEAD*...you see, ...a piece of equipment *DIDN'T* fall on it...

I see...... What d'you want me to believe, then?

Today...at the cottage...at lunch... ...in the woods........one of my secretaries..............

..threw a *cheese* at me.

Hmmn

OK, Stanhope.....I'll buy that.

In the office the next day, Janice & Dave are chatting.....

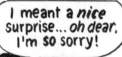